בס"ד

This book belongs to: לה׳ הארץ ומלואה

Please read it to me!

Shadow Play
A True Story of Tefillah

by *Leah Pearl Shollar*
illustrated by *Pesach Gerber*

Based on Taanit 23 a-b
and commentaries of the Rishonim.
Tehilim 121:5 and the commentaries
of the Baal Shem Tov

From Dan to Be'ersheva the wells were dry. No grain filled
the storehouses. All across the land people begged
Hashem for rain, but none came.

The Head of the Sanhedrin summoned Ploni and Almoni. "Honored gentlemen, please travel to the great Abba Chilkiya. We need him to ask for rain; Hashem always listens to his tefillos."

Ploni and Almoni set out on their journey. They traveled past cracked fields and weary flocks. Every living thing longed for cool, life-giving rain.

As Ploni and Almoni approached Abba Chilkiya's
door, a young boy holding a loaf of bread was thanking
the woman of the house.
She turned to Ploni and Almoni and asked,
"Would you like some bread or a little water?"
Gratefully, they each accepted a drink.

Ploni returned the cup. "The rabbis of Yerushalayim sent us to
find Abba Chilkiya, whose tefillos are always answered."
"My husband is not home," she said. "He works our neighbor's
field today." She pointed to the dry, wilting crops snaking
across the hills outside the city.

Ploni and Almoni hiked through the dust and heat, down steep roads and across parched fields until they reached a man hoeing a parcel of land.

Ploni picked his way over the rocks. "Excuse me sir, are you Abba Chilkiya?"

The man nodded but continued pushing and pulling his hoe. *Thwack*, he chopped up weeds, *clank*, he tossed stones in a pile. His breath came fast as he loosened the sandy soil.

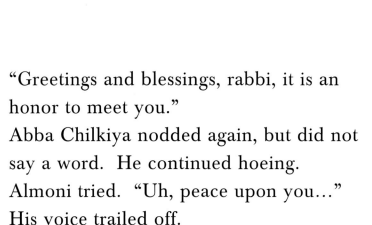

"Greetings and blessings, rabbi, it is an honor to meet you."
Abba Chilkiya nodded again, but did not say a word. He continued hoeing.
Almoni tried. "Uh, peace upon you…"
His voice trailed off.

He edged back toward Ploni.
"Why won't he answer us?"
"Do not question the rabbi.
He has his reasons," Ploni said.
"What are they?"
"Reasons," Ploni replied.

They waited in the shade of a
dried-up carob tree that rattled
when the wind blew.

As dusk's purple shadows settled over the terraced hills and roads, Abba Chilkiya stopped his work and unlaced his sandals.

"Please follow me home," he said. "We will discuss your business there."

Abba Chilkiya made his way to the main road, his sandals dangling from his fingers.

"Do what he does," Ploni urged.
Almoni nodded.
They rushed to untie their sandals and catch up with Abba Chilkiya.

The road was full of sharp rocks.
Ploni and Almoni lurched this way and that to avoid the stones and pebbles.
"Ouch!" Almoni cried out. He hobbled on his foot.
"Remember – the rabbi has his reasons," Ploni hushed.

Soon, they came to a muddy brook.
Abba Chilkiya laced up his sandals then plunged in!

Ploni and Almoni hurriedly tied their
sandals and splashed in after him.
"My sandals will be wet all night,"
said Almoni.

Ploni shrugged.
"Reasons," he said.

Abba Chilkiya turned off the road and pushed through a narrow path overgrown with sharp thorn bushes. He lifted his cloak, and the brambles brushed against his bare legs.

Ploni nudged Almoni. With a sigh, they lifted their cloaks and followed Abba Chilkiya, letting the prickly shrubs scratch their legs.
"Ouch!" Now Ploni cried out.

"You said the rabbi has his reasons," whispered Almoni. Ploni closed his eyes. "He does. I just don't understand them."

At last they reached Abba Chilkiya's home. His wife stood just outside the door. Abba Chilkiya whispered something to her, and then turned to Ploni and Almoni. "Please wait here, I will return in just a moment." Then he and his wife went inside.

Ploni and Almoni sat down across from the house and.
turned their faces up to the darkening sky. One by one,
the stars came out, glittering like crushed glass.

Just then two shapes flitted across the roof.
Abba Chilkiya stepped to one side, his
wife to the other. He lifted his hands; she
lifted hers.

In their separate corners, each begged
Hashem, "Bless us with dew and rain...
"Let us drink and be satisfied from Your
goodness, Hashem..."

Moments passed.
A cooling breeze
caught the edge of
Ploni's cloak, ruffled
Almoni's hair. They
smiled at each other.

Thick gray clouds gathered above Abba Chilkiya's wife. Thunder rolled toward them, then burst open the swollen clouds.

Rain at last!

Shivering from the sudden cold, Ploni and
Almoni ran to the house. How could the
tefillos have worked so quickly?
"I wonder – " Almoni began.

"Amazing, isn't it?" Ploni agreed. "How they
asked for rain, and just like that, it rained!"

Abba Chilkiya opened the door
and beckoned. "Welcome."
Inside, his wife bustled about, lighting the
oil lamps hanging from the walls.

"Shalom Aleichem, gentlemen.
How can I help you?" Abba
Chilkiya smiled warmly.

Ploni stepped forward. "Aleichem Shalom, esteemed rabbi. The Sanhedrin sent us to ask that you daven for rain. And we saw with our own eyes how quickly your tefillos brought life-giving waters! You have our deepest thanks."

Abba Chilkiya shook his head. "Give thanks for Hashem's goodness, He is the one who sends rain! But maybe you have other questions?"

Almoni spoke up. "Yes. Rabbi, why did you not answer us when we first greeted you?"

"Wonderful question! I am paid to work from sun-up to dusk, every minute of the day," said Abba Chilkiya. "Since this time does not belong to me, I cannot stop to chat with people. That would be stealing."
"Reasons," Almoni whispered.

Ploni lifted his tender foot. "Why did you go barefoot on the rocky paths, yet put on your shoes when you crossed the stream?"

Abba Chilkiya replied, "I have only one pair of shoes, I must make them last. On the road I can see any rocks and holes, so I do not need to wear shoes. But in the water, snakes and other creatures swim about, and I cannot see them at all.

Keeping myself safe is more important than protecting my shoes."
"Yes… Keeping safe…" Ploni repeated.

"But," said Almoni, pointing to his scratched
legs, "In the brambles you lifted your cloak,
letting the thorns scrape you.
Why not cover your legs?"

Abba Chilkiya pointed to his
own many scratches.
"These will heal."
He pointed to the cloak.
"This would need to
be mended.
I try not to make work
for others."

Almoni nodded. "I see now."

Ploni stood up. "One more question,
honored rabbi. You and your wife both
begged Hashem for rain. Why did the
clouds gather first above your wife?"

"Ploni, come and place your hand in front of this lamp.
What do you see?"
Ploni glanced at the wall where the shadow of his hand
loomed large. "My hand, and the shadow of my hand."

"Move your fingers. What do you see now?"
Ploni curled and unfurled his fingers. The shadows
curled and unfurled.
"The shadow follows my movements exactly."

Abba Chilkiya beamed at his wife.
"That is the secret," he said.
"Hashem is like our shadow.

"Because my wife acts with such kindness
toward those in need, Hashem does the same
for her... giving her whatever she needs,
whenever she asks."

They all gazed at the shadows
on the wall, none of them
speaking a word, but each
remembering how she
gave food to the poor.

Almoni nodded. "Hashem was her shadow. And ours, too.

"Hashem matches our every move and step. When we turn to help others, Hashem turns to hear our needs."

Abba Chilkiya smiled. "Now you know the secret of tefillah."

Ploni and Almoni thanked Abba Chilkiya and his wife, then pulled their cloaks closer and stepped into a veil of sparkling night rain.

Dedicated to our Beloved grandchildren:

Yosef, Chaim Zelig, Menachem Mendel, and Chana Tzivia
Esther, Yaccov, and Aliza Chana Tzivia
Esther Brocha Pessa and Yosef Yitzchak

Naftali and Molly Feldman
Bobby Rochel

First Edition – 5766/2006
Copyright © 2006 by HACHAI PUBLISHING
ALL RIGHTS RESERVED

Editor: D.L. Rosenfeld   Layout: Eli Chaikin

ISBN-13: 978-1-929628-21-6
ISBN-10: 1-929628-21-8   -   LCCN: 2005928730

HACHAI PUBLISHING
Brooklyn, New York - Tel: 718-633-0100 - Fax: 718-633-0103
www.hachai.com - info@hachai.com

Printed in China

For my children: Chaim, Ella, Masha, Esther Chana, Yissachar, and Manny.
May Hashem always be your shadow, granting you the wisdom to know what to ask for and the merit
to be answered graciously.
– Mommy

"Like Almoni and Ploni, most of us are looking for answers to many questions. Sometimes we travel afar
to find them...but more often they are found within the perceived shadows all around us."
– P.G.

Glossary

Aleichem Shalom	"Unto you, peace" (traditional response to greeting)
Hashem	G-d
Sanhedrin	The Jewish High Court
Shalom Aleichem	Peace be upon you" (a traditional greeting)
Tefillah, Tefillos (pl.)	Prayer(s)
Yerushalayim	Jerusalem